GRADE

02

PIANO

Pieces & Exercises for
Trinity College London
Exams 2018–2020

Published by
Trinity College London Press Ltd
trinitycollege.com

Registered in England
Company no. 09726123

Printed in England by Halstan & Co Ltd., Amersham, Bucks

The Marionettes

(duet part)

Stanisław Prószyński
(1926–1997)

The Marionettes

(candidate's part)

Stanisław Prószyński
(1926-1997)

Almost a Canon

Arr. Haas

Johann Joseph Fux
(1660-1741)

Allegro ♩ = 142

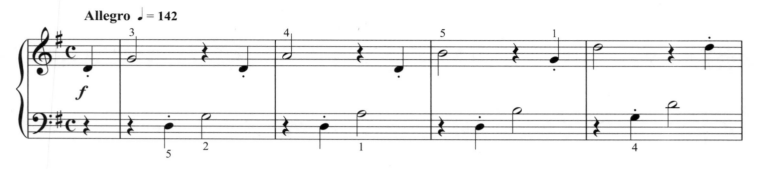

Rigaudon

Georg Philipp Telemann
(1681-1767)

Balletto

Arr. Haas

Georg Simon Löhlein
(1725–1781)

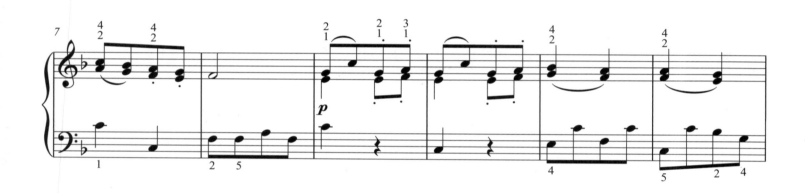

The Rowboat

Felicitas Kukuck
(1914–2001)

The Ballerina

Ray Moore
(b. 1939)

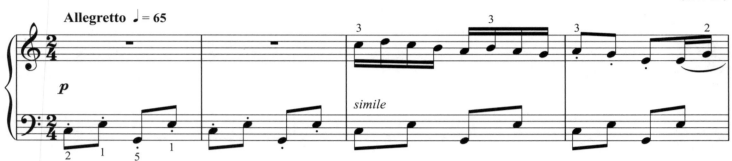

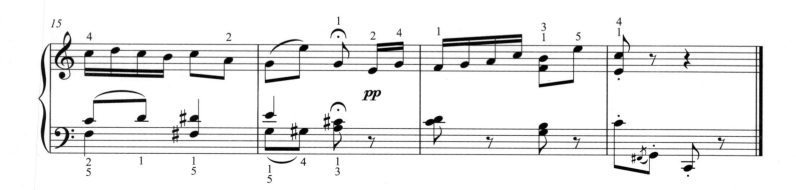

Shepherd's Melody

Rainer Mohrs
(b. 1953)

Do not play the repeat in the exam.

Persian Holiday

Sam Cleaver
(b. 1982)

Poor Mouse

Vera Mohrs
(b. 1984)

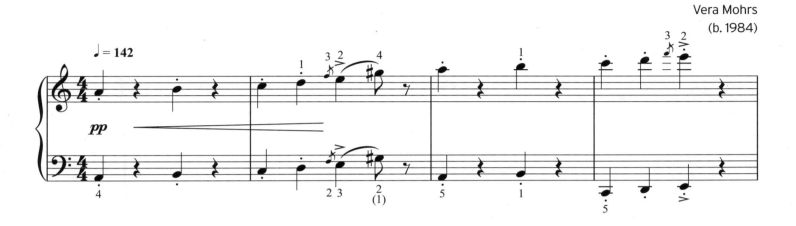

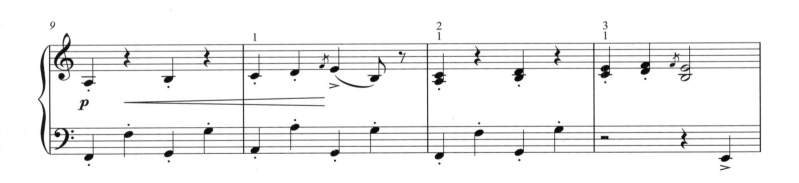

Exercises

1a. Handing Over – tone, balance and voicing

1b. A Baroque Formation – tone, balance and voicing

2a. Off-centre – co-ordination

2b. Quick March – co-ordination

3a. Late Night Lullaby – finger & wrist strength and flexibility

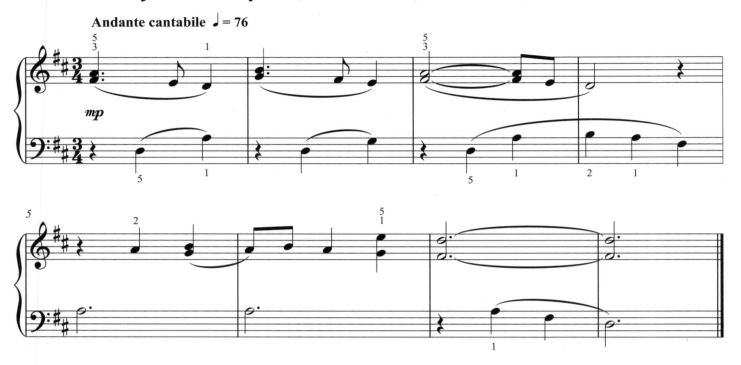

3b. Rockhopper – finger & wrist strength and flexibility